Angel In The Outhouse

Angel In The Outhouse

by

Kathya Alexander

Back Cover Photo Credit: Justice Beitzel

Cover Art Created by: Tully Murray

DISCLAIMER: This is a work of fiction. The people and events of the Civil Rights Movement are real, but times and/or circumstances have been changed to fit the story. Names, characters, businesses, places, events, and incidents are either the product of the author's imagination or used in a fictitious manner. Any resemblance to actual persons, living or dead, or actual events is purely coincidental.

Printed in the United States

First Edition, 2017

ISBN: 978-0-99983676-4-4 (paperback)

LCCN: 2017953284

With a Capital M Publishing Group, LLC
P.O. Box 52656
Durham, NC 27717
984-244-0793
www.withacapitalm.com
withacapitalm@gmail.com

Special discounts are available on quantity purchases by corporations, associations, and others. For details, contact the publisher at the address above.

to my roots
Rev. Freddie Louis Alexander
Mattie Lee Hull Alexander

and my suns
James Eric Lamonte Whitfield
Karioki Uhuru

Acknowledgements

I owe a huge debt of gratitude to the audience at Aunt Mama's Story Table at the Madison Park Starbucks in Seattle, who have come faithfully on the last Thursday of every month for over 10 years to listen to my stories as I created them. Whether they were good, bad, or mediocre, you have always been welcoming, full of grace, and ready to hear what I come up with next month. You are the best audience a storyteller could ever hope for, and you have made me better writer. I appreciate each and every one of you - especially those of you who have been there consistently from that very first story on that very first day.

I would also like to thank my storytelling partner-in-crime, Mary Anne Moorman (aka Aunt Mama), who tells the best Southern stories in the country and who has held The Story Table together with sheer force of will and determination for over a decade. And to Olubayo Johnson, the third "leg" of the Story Table, for stories so funny I laugh 'til my face hurts. I love you, Mathilda. We are truly a mutual admiration society!

To Cleo Brown and Natasha R. You inspire me.

Thanks to CLW for your encouragement early on, and for modeling that writing life.

To Shandra: Your support of this project touched me deeply. Thank you, Niecey Poo.

To Tyrone Brown: Your high expectations of me made me a writer. Thank you!

To LaMonda Sykes and With a Capital M Publishing, your professionalism and dedication to your writers has made this a memorable journey. Thank you, thank you, thank you for bringing my baby to life.

And to my family: My brother Lacy (LK) Alexander, who is always ready to tell me stories, and my brother Wardell Alexander, who holds the family history. And in memoriam to my siblings in heaven: LD, Berdine, Malvin, Dee, Libba, Mickey, and Erin Catherine. Your lives are the foundation on which I stand.

And to my suns, my greatest accomplishment. You always make me look good!

Table of Contents

'Naa Naa' excerpt published in Raising Lily Ledbetter: Women Poets Occupy the Workplace by Lost Horse Press

In The Garden

When A.D. come home,

he find Belle out in the truck patch.

Belle was sitting on her knees,

her mouth moving in prayer.

A.D. take a deep breath

and walk over to where she kneeling.

Somehow he know

she knowed everything then.

In one hand, she hold onto

the handle of a foot tub

she filling with tomatoes as she move

in and out of the rows.

In the other hand, she holding onto

a fat, ripe tomato.

She squeezing it so hard,

the juice run down 'tween her toes.

She had not notice him yet.

She somewhere inside of her head.

Trying to block out the image

she didn't have no right to see.

Trying to figure out what

she was gone do with her life.

Trying to figure out the best way

that she could strangle A.D.

"Dear Lord," Belle she cry out

silent to God,

"How I done been so blind

that I could not see

the thing that was going on

right in front of my eyes?

How I done lived a lie so long?

Dear Lord, answer me!"

"Belle?" A.D. say

as he walk up beside her.

"You looking kinda peaked.

Is you sho' you all right?"

Belle turn her head and throw up

all over his shoes.

Then she use her hand to wipe the vomit

from off of her mouth.

She been pulling the caterpillars

off the okra and tomatoes.

She bent over the vegetables.

 She pull herself up straight.

Her eyes hit A.D.

somewhere around 'bout his chest.

A.D. pick up the apples

she had pick for the cake.

The thought of her cooking

anything special for him

9

made her sick to her stomach.

Let alone cook a cake.

After what she had see'd

when she looked in that window,

she didn't care if A.D. starve.

Didn't care if he ate

nothing again.

Let his mama go feed him.

A.D. look at Belle.

He ask her again,

"You sho' you all right?"

"Why, sho', A.D. I'm just fine.

I ain't never felt this good

before a day in my life."

Her words dripping with venom.

A.D step back a big step.

Like he scared.

Like he don't know

what it is she will do.

Her hair all frizzed up

from the heat and her sweat.

Sticking out every which a way.

A.D. ask, "Can I do

something to help you lighten

your load just a little?"

Belle laugh out loud.

Laugh right there in his face.

"Why, yeah, I think

you can do something for me.
You 'kin tell me why you make
my life such a disgrace."
"What you mean, Belle?" A.D. ask.
Sweat form on his brow.
"What you thank I mean?"
Belle turn and she spit.
"I see'd you with that woman.
I see'd y'all out in the shed.
I see'd the way her hair was laying
all over your hip.
I see'd the nasty thangs
she done to you with her mouth.
I heard the way that you groaned
when you let loose of yo' seed."
"Belle, let me explain…"
"Explain what A.D.?
It ain't nothing to explain.
I knows what I see'd."

She bend over to the tomatoes
that hang low on the vine.
"The two of y'all was so busy,
you didn't even hear me.
Didn't even hear me stumbling
away from the shed.
In my head all I see
is her head 'tween yo' knees.

11

Dear Lord," Belle she call out

loud now to her God,

"How could I have been so blind

that I could not see?"

A.D. reach out his hand

to help Belle off her knees.

Belle sneer at him and say,

"Don't you never touch me, A.D.

Do you hear me, A.D.?

Don't never touch me again.

Yo' hand is as nasty

as a pile full of shit

that is covered with flies.

I don't know if I can bear

to have yo' hands on me.

No, not never again."

"Was a time when my hands

made you cry out with delight."

"Was a time when snakes had legs

and walked the earth like a dog.

Was a time when they didn't

have scales on they eyes.

Was a time when I thought

what we have is call love.

Was a time when I thought

the life that I live was mine.

The Devil is pretty, A.D.

Ain't you never heard it said?

Ain't you never knowed

why he was able to

tempt The Good Lord

the way that he did?

 The Devil put nasty in yo' face

and make you thank that you want it.

Then he make a lie out of everything

in yo' life you done lived."

"Belle, I didn't mean to hurt you.

I was just trying to…"

"Don't tell me what you was trying to do!

I knows what you did!"

"Well, don't nothing change the fact

that you my wife and I love you.

I know I was wrong.

But our life ain't changed to a lie.

I still love you as much

as I did when I met you.

Don't let this knowledge you got

come and destroy both our lives."

"Me, destroy?

You speak pretty words, A.D.

It was *you* in the orchard

doing unnatural acts.

And take yo' nasty hands

from out of my hair.

Carry that tub to the house.

Gone now. Get out of my face."

A.D. knowed it wasn't nothing

that he could say that would change

the set of her mind.

Or the set of her heart.

So he picked up the foot tub

with the okra and tomatoes

and carried them for her.

He set them on the back porch.

And then he left.

Belle stayed out in the garden.

Down on her knees praying

to God up above.

She cried 'til she couldn't

even cry no longer.

Then she start to put the armour

in place round her heart.

Delta Rose the only daughter

of a red-neck white lawyer.

Belle mama use to work

at they house when she well.

The white gal and Belle

wudn't really close in age.

But Belle play with her when her Mama

go to they house to sell

them the eggs and the butter

that she sell around town.
Mom Mattie add to they living
any way that she can.
She do cleaning when she able.
Wash and iron white folk clothes.
And Belle always go with her.
For as long as she can
remember back in her life,
she done work 'long side her Mama.
Cause Mom Mattie was weak.
Sick a lot of the time.
Belle had see'd A.D.
over to the white people house working.
But what she was seeing
slip right thru her eyes.

Delta Rose was round 'bout 11
when A.D. first meet her.
She was 15 and A.D. 11
the first time they have sex.
She had hair look like fire.
A.D. hadn't never see'd nothing like it.
He start to have them dreams about her
that make little boys sheets wet.
That was back when her daddy
and A.D. daddy, Levi,
have a run in over a tract of land
they both claim that they own.

It's the land they live on

now down near The Bottoms.

The dispute had been settle friendly.

So the families had done

business with each other

from time to time.

Over the years, A.D. start to do

little tasks round they house.

Levi Anderson talk that man

out of his land with a smile.

And Delta Rose take a liking

to A.D. from the start.

She the twinkle in her daddy eye.

And the thorn in his heart.

A.D. a shame-face little boy.

Shame round white folks anyway.

Delta Rose treat A.D. nice

'cause it bother her daddy.

She think it's some kind of fun.

It all start simple as that.

She was just slick enuf

to make they friendship look cute.

Like a attraction to the family cat.

Or for a stray dog

that come to the back door

looking for hushpuppies.

The first time they lay together

wudn't no reason but 'cause
Delta Rose want to have sex.
It start out innocent as that.
She was curious.
And A.D. was hard as a rock.
They both promise not to tell.
They both know what they do is dangerous.
That make it even mo' better.
A game they play every month
or so. Careful-like
so as not to cause no attention.
They was chi'ren. That ain't no excuse.
But it's the truth just the same.
If they had left it at a chi'ren's game,
no one would have got hurt.
It's the game they play when they grown
that's the sin and the shame.

If such a relation
become general knowledge,
the colored man in question
most likely be kill.
So I guess that's why it was hard
for Belle to believe
the danger A.D.
put hisself and her in.
Carrying on
with a rich white woman.

Everybody Down Home

know what is what.

Belle might have heard

some rumors about her husband.

But she don't put no stock

in no mess such as that.

But if you don't believe

your lying eyes,

life sho' do seem

to have a way

to show you the things

you don't want to see.

Like the Lord did to Paul

on his way to town one day.

Sometime the Lord will see you

on the back of a jackass

and blind you with a great light.

And then knock you down

on the side of a dusty

road somewhere.

He'll blind you and then

drop the scales from your eyes.

"Why I don't love *me*

more then I want him?

What was wrong with me

that I accept something like that?"

Even after they first dance,

Belle know now A.D. go to her.

Wasn't a time when she had
A.D. all to herself.

His flesh was on fire from
his first dance with Belle.
Delta Rose smell something like rainwater
on the hair 'neath his nose.
He had plan to tell her
that nite about Belle.
She make him want to become
something better than a roll
in the hay with a woman
he can't never love.
A.D. ain't stupid.
He know what is what.
But Delta Rose put money
in the book that she bring him.
That nite she give him
every cent that she got.
The money come in handy.
He can't say that it don't.
He keep all the money she give him
buried in a old croker sack.
And so he decide to tell her
about Belle the next time.
Then it was the time after that.
And then the time after that.

And now all them times

done got rolled into this time.

A.D. think real hard about

what it is he gone do.

He go pick up the chi'ren

from over to his mama's.

He bring them home and he bathe them.

Clyde, Vernell, and little Azra Lee too.

Belle got beans cooking

on the stove in the kitchen.

A.D. cook some cornbread.

That's all he know how to make.

His bread ain't like Belle's.

It's hard and taste kinda crunchy.

But that make it mo' better

to sop the bean juice up with.

The moon done rose

high up in the sky.

And Belle still ain't came in

from the truck patch where he left her.

The chi'ren keep asking him

where is they mama.

She ain't never not been there

when they was ready for bedtime.

A.D. listen to they prayers.

They all pray for they mama.

A.D. even offer up

a silent prayer too.

He ain't never been much

of a praying kinda man.

But if they family gone heal,

he know God gone have to do it.

Round 'bout midnight, Belle she finally

come back to the house.

"You all right?" A.D. ask

when she walk in to the door.

Belle act like he ain't even

opened up his mouth.

She just keep right on walking

cross the living room floor

and into they bedroom.

He go stand in the threshold.

He can see from where he standing

her eyes swollen from tears.

It break his heart that he done

caused her such a heartache.

He'd take back everything

if only he could.

But he know he can't.

He can feel it in her look

that go right past him.

Just over his shoulder.

While she changing from her day clothes

into her nite clothes,

he notice a grey streak in her hair.

She already look older.

"You want me to leave?"

A.D. he ask her.

"And go where, A.D.?

You going to yo' white woman?

Don't thank you gone get off

that easy A.D.

You got chi'ren to feed.

No, you ain't going nowhere.

Long as I got these chi'ren,

we gone live out this lie."

"My love for you ain't no lie, Belle,"

A.D. he tell her.

"Well my love for you

done just up and died."

"Don't do this, Belle.

We can make our lives better.

I promise you I ain't gone never

see that woman again.

We can start over.

The love we had can still keep."

Belle just look at him.

Then she pass gas real loud.

Then she turn over in the bed.

And she go to sleep.

Angel In The Outhouse

My mama say she have a son
get burn up one time in a fire.
I scratch this memory from out her scalp.
She in a chair. I stand behind her.
Dark done fell. Our lights is off.
Cause Daddy forget to pay the bill.
Mama know it is his payday
where he work down to the mill.
She say she do not know what could have happen.
He ain't showed up for her to ask.
My Daddy big. My Mama little.
But right now she could whip his a--.

I scratch a scab up from her head
and give it to her in her hand.
She say it bring to her remembrance
of that nite her son get dead.
She say this thing to me real quiet.
Voice so low my blood run cold.
That nite, she say, she get a scab too.
Not on her head. One on her soul.
She say wudn't no TV nor electric
way back when my brother die.
She say they use a lamp like this one

fill with kerosene all the time.
I want to ask what do they do
instead of watching My Three Sons.
But, I don't.
Instead I listen to her story just begun.

She say she wake up from a dream
and something tell her get straight up.
She rock and rock. Go back and forth.
And pray for now she know not what.
A spirit dance upon her ceiling.
Beckon for her come and play.
"Get out of here, you evil spirit.
Get out my heart," she say she say.
She see the spirit it just lightning
when she come back to herself.
Then thunder rattle pane in window.
She know she better rouse herself.
She push her feet from out the cover.
Slide one foot into a shoe.
She say she never did find the other.
Not with fire and Clyde death too.

She say she run all thru the house.
The nite so black feel like a touch.
She say, "Darkest hour come just foe day.
And 'member ain't so sucha thang as luck."

24

I do not know why Mama want me

to 'member this thing. But I say to her, "Yes, m'am."

She say, "The boys they sleep in one room.

The girls they sleep just like a lamb."

She say, "The fireplace it need stoking.

And the nite it get real cold."

"What y'all house look like?" I ask her.

She say, "Like this one. 'Cept with mo' doors.

It have a fireplace. Not like this one.

Seem like white folk only have them now."

I wonder why it seem po' coloreds

can't seem to get ahead no how.

She recollect how fear come on her.

Gnaw at her skull just like a rat.

"You know what that like?" she turn and ask me.

"I know what rat like. Turn yo' head back."

She say she know some thang ain't right.

But, she say, she cannot see.

She scream, "Get up!" into the darkness.

"Cleo! Clyde! Azra Lee!

Get up. Get out right now!" she holler.

Then she run where girls is sleep.

Vernell and CeCe in the kitchen.

They resting calm as they can be.

I like for Mama to tell me stories

'bout way back when my brother die.

Cause back then I wudn't even a twinkle

what shine in my Daddy eye.

My brother, Cleo, he real little.

He grown now. He live in Los Angeles.

He drink a lot and act a fool.

He keep my mama on her knees.

He ball his fist up and he hit me

last time that he come home to stay.

Just cause the way I bring him water

ain't fast enuf to suit his taste.

I ask my Mama do she remember

that time when Cleo in a fight.

One time when he go to the juke joint.

Back off in the woods one Sat'dy nite.

I like the part 'bout how that man

raise Cleo way up in the air.

(I hear this story from his friends.

Of course, you know I wasn't there.)

Say razor come out Cleo's sock

so fast it look like it was greasy.

Cleo stutter and he say,

"Puu-ut me down easy. I mean rr-real easy."

My Mama frown and grunt. She say,

"Shoot, Cleo nice as any other

til L'il Man get hit by that truck."

Mama say that change my brother.

My brother Azra Lee he die

from something happen in the war.

My Mama wrap his pipes and medals
up in silk. They in a drawer.
I hear her take them out and cry
sometime when I lay wake at nite.
I make him a get well card when he get sick.
And people shock that I can write.

I go stay with my Cousin Cece
in St. Louis when school get out.
My Mama raise her cause her mama
she too busy stepping out.
Her son a big old stanky cry baby
by the name of David Earl.
He get on my last nerve sometime
because he act just like a girl.
My cousin call pinto beans 'brownies'
like she think they is a treat.
I get so excited the first time she say that.
I'm so surprise come time to eat!

Vernell I do not like at all.
She try to act like she my Mama.
Hit her one time up side her head
with mop so hard she start to holler.
"Whip yo' own," my Mama tell her.
"Send her to me she show out."
I stick my tongue out at Vernell.
Mama backhand me so quick

she knock the spit from out my mouth.

"No electric show don't help
arthritis none," my Mama say.
She rub her knee. Same one she hurt
on roll'way bed that nite she say.
She say she drag the girls out one door
just as she hear another slam.
She think all the boys safe on the back porch
once she hear the door go blam!
But, she say, *something* about the sound
that try to tell her thangs ain't right.
But, she say, she do not follow
her first mind that awful nite.
She look at me and she say, "Mandy,
all way follow yo' first mind."
I say "Yes, m'am." And then I part
her thick grey hair in a long straight line.
She say, "Don't never love a man so much
that you can't tell when he is lying."
I scratch some dander from out her scalp.
I do not think she know she crying.
"Damn you," she say just like she do
when she come home and lights is off.
"Daddy gone the nite Clyde die."
I ask her, "Where?"
Her voice get soft.
She look into the lamp beside her.

Adjust it so it don't go dead.

"Do it hurt?"

She whisper, "No."

I mean her heart.

She mean her head.

Damn you, A.D. she scream at her husband

when she find the two in bed.

She remember all the times she found

the long red hair from the woman's head

on A.D. clothes. She don't pay them no mind.

She think she and the woman friends.

'Til she walk in on them out in the shed.

Candles burning soft and dim.

A.D. he cover up his butt

and push the white gal to the floor.

Belle close her husband out her heart.

And slam the door forevermore.

She run out the shed into the orchard.

She scream the way a banshee might.

Her whole world fall down round her knees

on that warm October nite.

She feel the air go still around her.

Then the lightning strike the house.

"This the sound it make," she tell me.

"*Craaack!*" She make the sound back in her mouth.

She say she stand with her mouth open

29

and watch the fire eat up the roof.

When she come back to herself

she covered up with smoke and soot.

She say, "Just then Cleo and Azra

come round the corner from side the house."

She say she still don't know Clyde missing

'til Azra Lee open up his mouth.

He ask her, "Mama, where my brother?"

Mama say the baby said.

She look back at the house and she know.

Her oldest child is good as dead.

Another streak light up the sky.

She turn and see Clyde in the window.

Mouth shape in his Mama name.

He calling for her, "Come and get me!"

She say she never will forget

the look of fear upon Clyde face

just before the house fall down.

And turn itself into Clyde grave.

Then she quiet. And you know

my Mama forget I stand behind her.

I scratch her scalp real soft.

And up come big ole flake of juicy dander.

She get him out somehow or 'nother.

She don't know how she say to me.

She pick her son up in her arms

and set him down by the old oak tree.

He scream her name out 'til he die.

Skin burnt so bad it's black and smooth.

The Chi'ren Who Live scream out behind her.

But, she say, she cannot move.

"Lord, please have mercy on my soul!"

All nite long my Mama beg.

She stay this way 'til Daddy find them.

He reach for her. She bite his leg.

She say she like a dog who mad.

Her mouth all full of spit and foam.

I cannot 'magine this my Mama.

I wipe the dander from off the comb

and put my finger to the soft spot on her head.

She start to moan.

I rub her scalp real soft and easy.

Careful so the nail don't rub.

"How long you stay that way?" I whisper.

"Until the day the angel come."

A pain, she say, shoot thru her butt

and make her come back to herself.

She in her daddy bed she say.

She smell like she done soil herself.

She don't know just how long she been there.

But she know it must have been a while.

Cause she can smell the honeysuckle.

It smell so sweet it make her smile.

She crawl up out the bed she lay in.

Stomach cradle in her palm.

No one at home she say she reckon.

Cause the house real nice and calm.

She say she look round for her shoes,

but she don't find none for her feet.

So she walk barefoot to the toilet.

In pain so bad it make her weep.

The darkness wrap itself around her.

The grey wood cool beneath her feet.

She heish her skirt up round her waist

and set down on the wooden seat.

Bitterness roll from her eyes.

She hurt so bad she start to moan.

The pain cut thru her like a razor.

The scream in her throat sound like a song.

"Blessed Father up in heaven.

Have mercy on me, if you please."

She need to get up off the toilet.

She need to fall down on her knees.

"Help...me...Lord, I cry to Jesus.

Hear yo' servant humble call."

She turn to me. Say, "'Member all way,

God He catch you when you fall."

What happen next my Mama say

she never tell a living soul.

She say a hand reach out and grab her.

And just like that! her pain is gone.

She say a woman stand before her.

Bright and shiny as the sun.

She say the angel speak and say,

"I come from God. His will be done."

When angel speak she say she hear it

not in her ear. But in her soul.

I say, "It must be sorta like

the nite you hear the thunder roll."

"Yes," she say. "It just like that."

"Was you scared?" I want to know.

She say her knees was almost buckling.

My Mama say she scared for sho'.

"God send me to you with a message,"

Mama say the angel say.

"And what's this message so important

you come to my outhouse today?"

She say she just can't help but laugh.

This 'bout as foolish as thangs come.

"Forgive," she say the angel say.

Then poof! Like that! The angel gone.

"What she want you to forgive?"

I ask my Mama. Her voice get low.

"Myself," she say. "Yo' Daddy too."

For what is what I like to know.

I'm quiet while I think on this.

Mama quiet too, I see.

She sit and stare off into space.
And rub that old wound on her knee.

God could just as soon have ask her
walk on water. Part the sea.
She don't remember back in time
when 'forgive' a thing she want to be.
What it feel like she not lukewarm?
If she say just what she meant.
She wonder what have happen to her.
She wonder where her passion went.
She hold her hand up to her nose
and breathe, although its clog with snot.
Her breath come out just like she know.
It come out neither cold nor hot.
She know she do not hate her husband.
That would mean she have to care.
The way she got her life set up
caring is something she just don't dare.
Apathy spread so far and wide
it make her pie crusts gummy.
And her cakes don't rise.
I love you, he says.
His touch make her jake
her body back from him
like she bit by a snake.
That don't make him quit reaching.
She can't say that it do.

34

He just sing Baby Belle, Baby Belle

to the tune of the blues.

He bring her persimmons.

She spit in his face.

He give the 'simmon pits to the chi'ren.

But the knife and fork he leave in place.*

"What you say then, Mama?"

"Show me how," she say she say.

And then my mama tell me,

"Member God will all way show the way.

All you got to do is ask Him.

Just look at me," my Mama say.

Just then the lights all come back on.

And the furnace start to hum.

Daddy walk in thru the front door.

Two bags of grocery in his arms.

"Be glad the Lord He touch my heart, A.D."

my Mama say. Her voice all mean.

"And that I is, Baby Belle, Baby Belle.

God know I is!" my Daddy sing.

*In Black Southern legend, special persimmon pits have a carved knife and

fork in their center

In Bloom

Belle put her fingers in the ground.

She breathe in the dark odor.

The dirt under her hands

done turn her nails a black color.

She take the seeds out the box

where she done place them with care.

She rub the grey of the stone.

Then she take a sniff of the air.

The air smell wet like the dirt.

Cool and moist. Almost crisp.

She take a handful of dirt

and let it run down thru her fist.

The tears on her face

drop onto the black earth.

The soil look like its mixed

with some oil, it's so dark.

The dirt feel kinda gravelly.

Full of pebbles and grit.

She rub the dirt on her fingers

right down to the tips.

She raise her hand so she can wipe

the tears from out of her eyes.

She had not been to this place
since her child had first died.
It remind her of when
she first laid Clyde in the grave.
That day the sun wasn't shining.
It feel a lot like today.
Like the whole sky was heavy
with the grief in her heart.
She had not known how she'd make it.
And almost didn't sometimes.
Especially during those days
after he had first died.
If it wudn't for the angel,
she probably could not have gone on.
For a while the only thing
that keep her alive was her hatred.
For A.D. And for that red-headed
woman he laid with.

A.D. hand her the Starflower.
Then he get down on one knee.
It remind her of
the first time that she
told him that she knew.
They was in a garden then too.
She had close her heart that day.
Shut the door on love too.

37

But she stayed. Lord, she stayed.

She had four chi'ren then alive.

Vernell was the baby.

Then Azra Lee. And then Clyde.

Plus she was raising Cece.

In her heart, she was her own.

Even tho she wudn't Cece's mama,

Belle couldt'na loved that chile more

if she had borne her under her breast

like she had her own chi'ren.

Cece was the chile that gave

the best of her back to her.

"Is you all right?" A.D. say.

It was the same thing

he say to her when he find her

out in the garden

that first time. Back then,

before she harden her heart,

the sound of him walking up on her

would give her such a start.

It was a game that they play.

To see if he could *not* scare her.

When she had her hands in the dirt,

she was always so much in her head that

she would jump near a foot

whenever someone come up behind her.

But mostly A.D.

38

He walk so soft on the ground then.

"I'm fine, A.D."

Belle she say as she push

the seeds in the box

over to A.D. with her foot.

He lay a towel on the ground

so that his pants don't get dirty.

Sometime A.D. seem to act

so much more like a lady

than Belle ever done.

She like the dirt on her knees.

Like the feeling that come over her

when she feel her bones squeeze

the soil beneath her skin.

A.D. take the seeds out the box.

But first he put on his gloves.

He like to keep his hands soft.

Belle's hands full of calluses.

From cleaning white ladies' houses.

A.D. a janitor too.

But his hands soft, while hers is

not. It's ok now.

It's just another one of them things

that make Belle marvel at how

they been together for all these years.

The sky growing darker.

Clouds is off in the distance.

The sun going down.

And they still is not thru yet.

Belle want to get these seeds planted

while its enuf light for to see.

She take another bag from the box.

A.D. take one too, but then he

look at Belle and he say,

"Why we don't do this no more?

Work in the garden together.

Like we used to before…"

Then his voice trail off.

He don't finish his thought.

Belle finish it in her head.

Before you tear 'part my heart.

A fat raindrop fall out

of the sky on her cheek.

It mix with the tears from her eyes.

She open her mouth up to speak.

She mean to tell A.D. to hurry.

But the words that come out is this.

"A.D., I done love you

so long that it hurt."

"I never meant to hurt you, Belle.

Never meant a lot of things."

"I done learn to forgive."

Just like the angel had said.

"I don't deserve your forgiveness.

But I appreciate it just the same."

Another raindrop fall in her hair,

thick as a mane.

"We better get this job finish.

It is starting to rain."

A.D. say, "You think the day will come

when you will love me again

like you use to love me

before the bad thangs they come?"

"I done love you enuf to bear you

three daughters and six sons."

She done buried another chile

besides this one and Clyde.

He the only one of her dead chi'ren

to live to become a grown man.

And now she pregnant again.

She ain't told A.D. yet.

They just put one child in the ground.

A girl who die of crib death.

It is her grave that they planting

flowers on on this day.

And Belle know in her heart

she won't never see it again.

But she will leave something beautiful.

Something that will last forever.

They planting Daisy Gloriosas.

That's the same name as the baby.

Daisy Gloria.

She only live seven days.

She never did look healthy.

Not to Belle anyway.

She was too beautiful to live.

That's what Belle always say.

They choose the flowers for the dreams

both of them have for the baby.

So they planting Blanket Flowers.

Cause Belle always want her to be warm.

Belle reach down and push

the wildflower seeds in the soil.

She also plant Forget Me Nots.

Cause Belle will always remember

holding this child to her breast.

And breathing in her sweet smell.

All the flowers they planting

will come back year after year.

The seeds will fall back down to the earth

and will all bloom again.

But Belle won't never know.

This the last time she plan to see

her daughter's grave again.

Cause it don't hold her child's spirit.

She also plant some Blazing Star.

Cause that's where Belle want to see her.

A bright star in the sky

when she look up to the heavens.

The rain falling steady now.
It's coming down a little harder.
Belle take out the last packet
of seeds and she hold them
in her hand.
These ones is called Jacob's Ladder.
She pick that one in case the baby
need help getting to heaven.
A.D. plant Jack In The Pulpit
cause of him being a preacher.
He also plant A Knight In White Satin
cause that was his dream for his daughter.
Belle coulda told him
ain't no sucha thang as a knight
who come to your rescue,
all shiny and bright.
That's a white gal's fairy tale.
Belle is sho' of that now.
A colored woman can't expect nothing
except heartbreak and sorrow.

"We can be happy again.
Even after all of this time,"
A.D. he say to her.
Belle keep her eyes to the ground.
"I don't expect happy,"

Belle she finally say.

"All I want is for God to stop treating

my heart like its His play

thing. But I know what I want

don't make God one bit of difference."

She hear a clap of thunder rolling

from somewhere way off in the distance.

She pat the last of the dirt

onto the top of the grave.

She try to stand up

and A.D. hold out his hand.

She give her hand to him.

And he smile like a fool.

Forgive. That's what the angel

had told her to do.

And she done tried to do that.

With every beat of her heart.

Put all of her energy into keeping

her family from falling apart.

That was over 20 years ago.

She done forgive. But not forget.

She look at A.D.

and see that his face is all wet.

So they hold each other and cry.

Both of them drowning in grief.

They done got the headstone laid.

And planted wildflowers from seeds.

All of a sudden the heavens open.

Rain fall down like a sheet.

They run to the car.

Both they clothes soaking wet.

A.D. turn on the heater

so the windows defrost.

Belle look out her side

at the work they accomplished.

The headstone is shining.

Even in spite of the rain.

And the ground is opening

its mouth as if saying,

I receive this water

so all your dream flowers will grow.

Whoever pass by Daisy's

gravesite from now on

will be overcome by the colors

of Wild Ginger and Morning Glory.

And the Fringed Blue Star

and the Violet Blue-eyed Mary.

The Passion Flower and Mist Flower,

the Blue Hearts and Butterfly Pea.

"Planting these flowers has been

a real blessing to me,"

Belle say to her husband.

He look over and smile.

"I'm glad," he say.

He reach out and cover her hand

with his own. Belle she sigh

way deep down in her chest.

As they leave the cemetery for the last time,

Belle sing under her breath.

> *Tis the old ship of Zion*
>
> *Tis the old ship of Zion*
>
> *Tis the old ship of Zion*
>
> *Get on board*
>
> *Get on board*
>
> *It will carry you to heaven*
>
> *It will carry you to heaven*
>
> *It will carry you to heaven*
>
> *Get on board*
>
> *Get on board*

Naa Naa

She wake up in the blackness.
The darkest hour of the day.
Just before the Lord come
and roll the nitetime away.
She the color of nite.
Her skin stretched tight
across her face.
And the veins on her hands
tell the whole story of her life.
She sit on the slop jar by the bed.
She careful not to wake
the sleeping body beside her.
Miz Irma, her housemate.
She ain't never been married.
Never had chick nor chile.
Miz Irma is the only
kinda family she got.
Beside us, that is.
We not blood or nothing neither.
But Mama say she help them
when they first move to the city
from Down Home.
I don't know what it is that she done.
But it make Mama make her family

whatever it was.

She live with us when I was little.

I call her Naa Naa.

I remember when she move

to the little house in Galloway.

The house have two rooms and a kitchen.

And it have a little porch.

And the gray shingles on her house

look as old as she was.

She heish her gown over her head.

And she get dressed in the dark.

She run her hand over the few strands

of hair she got left.

Then she tie a headwrap around it.

And put her straw hat on.

To protect herself from the scorching

heat of the burning sun

that she know is coming.

She eat biscuits and molasses for her first meal.

Then she get the beans and cornbread in the tin can

that she carry out to the fields

for her lunch. Pretty soon she know

the cotton picking truck gone be coming.

She running late this morning.

So she know she need to hurry.

It's already after 3 o'clock.

She usually ready by now.

She put her hands on her back

and she stretch herself out.

She gone be bent over all day long.

Her knees is already creaking.

She look over to the bed

where Miz Irma lay sleeping.

She wish she could lay back down.

She think she must be getting old.

She set the wheelchair beside the bed

for Miz Irma when she wake up.

And she thank God that she got knees

that still able to creak.

"Thank you, Lord," she say,

whispering under her breath,

"for health and strength that you give me.

For two hands for to work."

If she lay her troubles beside another,

she always pick hers back up.

She pull her stockings on

and tie a knot at the knees.

Then she put on her brogans,

run over at the heels.

She go sit out on the porch

while she wait for the cotton truck to come.

In the sky, she look

for the first tinge of the sun.

But the sun is still sleeping.

Ain't got to need to come up yet.

Ain't nothing out this early

but colored folks and the white

folks who carry them to work.

The sun come up when it please.

She ain't never in her life

done woke up with such ease

as the sun rise in the morning.

She think about that song that say,

'that lucky old sun that ain't got nothing to do

'cept roam around heaven all day.'

She flex her arthritic hands

and rub the rheumatiz in her knees.

Then she get her cotton sack from behind

the cupboard where she keep it.

Work is the only thing

that she done ever knowed.

And, if she lucky, she gone work

'til the day she dead and gone.

Heaven, to her,

is a place to go rest.

She want to see her Mama too.

She ain't never knowed her daddy.

Some white men kill him

when she still a lap baby.

She go to work when she three

to help put food on the table.

That's when she first start chopping cotton.

Her mama make her a little hoe.

And she done worked ever since.

Work is all that she know.

The cotton truck drive up

and she get up off the porch.

She pull herself in the back

and she say hello to the other

colored women in the truck.

Clara, Nootie, and Sarah.

It's mostly men on the truck.

Too many to mention.

All told, it's 'bout 20 or 30

colored folks in the back.

The white man driving the truck

name of Old Mr. Jack.

"How Miz Irma this morning?"

Nootie and Clara both ask.

 "She feeling kinda po'ly.

Didn't sleep worth a damn."

"I made some root tea for her.

Make sho' she drink it tonite."

And Nootie hand her a jar

in a brown paper sack.

"Thank you kindly," Naa Naa say.

"How y'all doing this morning?"

Nootie say, "Clara almost couldn't

get away from her husband."

"Hush yo' nasty mouth,"

Miz Clara she say.

"Ain't nothing wrong with yo' husband

wanting to have his way…"

Both them women is crazy.

They got her laughing from the start.

It make it easier to work

when you got a smile in your heart.

That's what her mama always tell her.

And she done learned it's the truth.

If working is yo' life,

seem like it's better if you

find the goodness in it.

Even in the worst of times

she can find something in the day

that is fit to make her smile.

She ain't never understood them people

who complain and carry on.

You do what you gotta in life.

You just do it and go on

with yo' head held high.

With a song in your breast.

Going in and out the rows,

that song seem to carry

her on thru the day.

Even when her back is breaking.

Even when the strap on the cotton sack

she hauling is weighing

more than she do.

She always pick more than 500 pounds.

She a little bitty woman.

No bigger than a 10 year old child.

She fly thru the rows

which is longer than a mile.

Her hands flying thru the bolls,

sweat falling in her eyes.

She wipe the sweat off her brow

with the 'kerchief round her neck.

She pick her first 100 lbs

before the sun even up.

By the time the sun hang

straight up in the sky,

she'll be near 500 lbs.

And so tired she almost crying.

Some folks try to trick the scales.

They put dirt and rocks in they sack.

But she proud that she always

do a honest day's work.

She gone be out there all day.

'Til near 'bout 5:00.

That's when she pass on the highway

that run in front of our house.

I wait in the front yard

for the truck to come by.

She throw some money out the back

in a hankerchief she got tied

up in a knot.

I pick up the hankerchief from the ground.

I jump up and down

when I see her bright smile.

I wave my hands and I call out,

"I love you, Naa Naa.

Thank you very much!"

And I throw her kisses

from the tips of my outstretched fingers.

Her lips mouth the words,

"You so welcome, my baby."

I can't hear no sound

but I know what she saying.

We been doing this ritual

for years and years already.

I turn and go in the house,

the coins in the hankerchief jingling.

She settle back in the seat,

the paper sack in her lap.

She done caused joy in this day.

And that make it all worth it.

Casting Lots

I'm reading my book
of Bible Stories.
My Daddy sitting in
the big dining room chair.
He getting his sermon ready
for church service tomorrow.
And the story I'm reading
is about the same thing.
Me and my Daddy
do this every Saturday.
He start finishing up his sermon
right after dinner.
That's when I iron
his handkerchiefs.
Most times I have to
iron about 20
that he go thru
while he preaching his sermon.
I count them down every Sunday
when he is preaching.
Soon as my daddy
start to sweating,
his stack of handkerchiefs

start to shrinking.

The way he wipe

his face each time

and throw the handkerchief

to the side

is part of a rhythm

that my Daddy got

as part of his regular

preaching style.

After I get thru

ironing his handkerchiefs,

I join my Daddy

in the dining room.

"What your sermon about

tomorrow?" I ask him.

He kiss me on my jaw

that look just like his.

Daddy tell me he is going

to preach about Esther.

So I find her story

in my Bible Stories book.

The picture it show

is of a woman who is dressed

in beautiful clothes.

Holding her hand out.

A king with a crown

upon his head

is holding out his staff

to the beautiful lady.

They almost look like white people.

Almost but not quite.

I like these Bible stories

cause they

have people who

look like me

sometime when I turn to

the illustrations.

Well not look like me

but almost the same color.

All the other Bible stories

books I have

got people who is white

and most of them is blond.

This Esther have dark hair.

And her eyes is brown.

Another thing I like

is the illustrations is in color.

And they have all color people

on the bright blue cover.

When I get thru reading

I go over to Daddy.

He always put

his pen and paper down

and place his finger

on his spot in the Bible.

He kiss me again.

He do that a lot.

"All right,

tell me about the story."

That's what my Daddy

always say.

Sometimes I get

the story wrong.

But I think I got

it right today.

I say, "The story is really about

this man name Mordecai.

To me Esther is almost

like a secondary character."

"Is that so?"

my Daddy say.

"Yeah. Seem like she got caught up

in her uncle's business.

Cause Esther was minding

her own self business.

She was perfectly happy

with the life she had.

Until her uncle

came and got her."

"All right. So tell me the story,"

my Daddy say again.

I climb up on

my Daddy's lap.

This is my favorite

place to be.

He grunt as he position me

on his legs.

"You getting too big."

Daddy always say that to me.

I say, "The King had a wife

who made him mad

cause she didn't come

when he told her to.

Cause she was having a party

with some of her friends.

So he banished her

and started looking to

find another woman

who would come when he called.

And he asked his assistant

whose name was Haman

to help him find

the right kind of woman.

And this man name Mordecai

overheard it.

And since Mordecai had

a beautiful niece,

he figured he should

throw her into the pot.

And since Mordecai

worked right in the palace,

he got the folks he worked with

to hook Esther up

and dress her in the stuff

that the King liked best.

Showered her in all

the King's favorite perfume.

So when the King was

picking over all the women,

he smelled Esther before

she even walked in the room.

And he picked her

to be his new queen.

Stay in the harem where

the King keep his women."

(I ask Daddy one time

about all of that,

and he just say that's how

it was in Egypt.)

"Well, Haman and Mordecai

met up somewhere,

and Haman told Mordecai

to bow down.

But them Hebrews don't

bow down to nobody except God.

And when he wouldn't

Haman got real mad

and decided he was gone

kill all the Jews."

(See things like this

I do not understand.

That's how white people

do Negroes too.

One Negro do something

and every Negro bad.)

"But the killing got to be done

on a particular day,

so Haman had his wizards

and prophets and whatnot

to come up with

the perfect date.

And them people chose the date

by casting lots."

The picture they showed

at the beginning of the story

was of Queen Esther

holding out her hand

to the King.

And the King didn't kill her.

He told her to

come right on in.

And it wasn't like Esther

was even in love with the man.

She just was doing
what her uncle told her.
So she went to the King
and flounced around
until she got him to
take a look at the document
that Haman had made
her husband sign.
"The miracle was that Esther
did not get killed,"
I tell my Daddy.
"Cause back then folks
didn't just walk into the office
to see the King.
When the King found out
that Haman had tricked him
and made him sign something
he didn't understand
the King lynched Haman
on the same tree
that he had built
for Mordecai and
all the Jews.
So God protected His people.
And He used Esther
to pull it off."
That's the story
I told to my Daddy.

He listen to everything

I said *real* hard

and then he said,

"That was the perfect story.

I want you to preach it

tomorrow at church."

"Me preach the sermon?

I can't do that."

"Yes, you can,"

my Daddy answer back.

"You just tell

the Bible story

the same way you just

told it to me."

"For real?" I say.

"For real," Daddy answer.

And that is how

 it came to be

that I preach my first sermon

in Daddy's pulpit.

Mama comb my hair

and fix it up in a ball.

I think I look

real sophisticated.

Just like my Daddy do

when he preach the Word of the Lord.

I guess you know

I was real excited.

This the first grown thing
that I done ever done.
Daddy even give me
a new handkerchief.
It was sparkling white
with lace all around it.

When I walk up to
the big wood podium,
Deacon Jones put a stand
behind the lectern.
I step up on
the wooden block.
So I don't have no trouble
seeing over the pulpit.
I look straight at
the audience faces.
I bow my head
and start with a prayer.
That's what my Daddy
always do.
The whole congregation say
a big "A-man."

I tell the
story of Esther
just like I tell it to Daddy
in the dining room.

I end my talk

by saying that

what I learned is that

the Living God

who rose on

Easter Sunday morning

in the form of

His Son Jesus Christ

knew what would happen

to His chosen people

way before Haman thought

about casting lots.

The whole congregation

stand on they feet.

"Aman! Aman!"

the congregation call.

I use my handkerchief

to dab the sweat

off my top lip

while I am preaching my sermon.

Then Daddy take over

and put the 'whoop' on it.

Miz Sims and Miz Ella Mae

start to shouting.

Cause they all feel like

they God's chosen too.

Regardless of what

it say in the Bible

about Jews and all.

Cause we all Negroes.

Who have borne the brunt

just like the Jews.

I think the church really like

my sermon about Esther.

My Daddy smile a lot.

And I do too.

A-a-a-man,

A-a-a-a-man

Aman, Aman

A-a-a-man

The Wedding

"I want Mandy to be in my wedding,"
Evelyn say to Mama. She in our living room.
"I want her to be a junior bridesmaid
when I get married this coming June."
"And what is all of this gone cost me?"
my Mama say. Evelyn answer her back,
"Just buy the dress," Evelyn say to Mama.
"And I'll take care of everything else."
"Everything else?" my Mama say.
"What else is it for you to get?"
"I'll get the socks and bows and shoes.
I want to make sure that everything matches."
I hear Miz Wendy say to my Mama
that she think Evelyn trying to act too uppity.
"Trying to put on airs with this fancy wedding.
Like Evelyn is not one of them Thompsons."

Mr. Thompson is Uz's most pitiful drunk.
He get so drunk he cannot stand.
I done seen him fall down in the ditch.
That always make Carol Jean and Beverly Ann
real shame when he do stuff like that.
Everybody in school tease them about it.

But they laugh at Mr. Thompson theyself.

What else you gone do when you got somebody like that for a daddy?

"I hope he don't even come to the wedding,"

Carol Jean tell me. We was sitting in my tree.

She like to climb trees like I do.

Sometimes she go even higher than me.

But I don't care if Mr. Thompson come to the wedding.

If he sit down somewhere like he know how to act.

When he ain't drunk, he just sit in his bedroom.

So at the wedding I hope he act like that.

"It's a crying shame," my Mama always say

about Mr. Thompson. And not just cause he be drunk.

Sometime he beat on Miz Thompson too.

I ain't never seen nobody else who beat on they wife.

He just do that cause Miz Thompson so nice.

I already seen the dress that Evelyn get her.

It's the dusty color of a pale pink rosebud.

And it's got a lot of antique lace all over it.

I can't wait to see my dress.

I get so excited when Evelyn describe it.

She say the lace on the top the same color as Miz Thompson.

And she say I got to wear a petticoat up under it.

I love wearing petticoats! My Mama don't like it.

She say when I wear 'em, I flounce around too much.

Just cause I like to spin around in a circle

and make my pretty dress flare out.

"My wedding colors are dark and light pink.

The dresses are on hold downtown at Blass.

They're the prettiest things. Mandy, you're gonna love it.

It's got a empire waist and a pink satin sash."

This wedding the biggest thing Uz done ever seen.

Most people marry at home when they get married.

Jake and Dara get married on our front porch.

It was pretty and all, but it was still a small wedding.

Evelyn she getting married down to St. Luke at the church.

To a man name Kendall Ray Livingston.

His family is from somewhere up north.

I think maybe Flint. Or maybe Detroit.

Kendell he is in the Army.

He drive a Mustang. And his family rich.

His daddy work for General Motors.

And when he get out the Army, he gone work there hisself.

Evelyn she got 20 people

who is a part of her wedding party.

It's 3 bridesmaids and 3 junior bridesmaids,

plus a best man and a matron of honor.

She got a boy to walk with every girl.

But she got two flower girls and only one ring bearer.

And she got the same dress as Jackie Kennedy have.

'Cept Miz Kennedy's was long and Evelyn's ankles is showing.

She even got the same five-tier wedding cake.

And they gone even have champagne to drink.

I ain't never seen nobody have champagne at they wedding.

I only seen that in weddings that be on TV.

The whole week before the wedding,

I been helping Carol and Beverly make the decorations.

We put some rice in a piece of pink lace.

And then we make some tissue paper carnations.

The rice is for people to throw at the wedding.

Mama say the rice is for good luck.

Everybody gone get a little rice sack.

After we put the rice in the lace, we tie it up

with a little piece of pink satin ribbon.

Evelyn even got pink mints and pink frappe.

That's what people gone have at the reception.

She gone hold it down in St. Luke's basement.

She even got the same wedding song

that Jackie Kennedy have at her wedding.

Miz Victoria is singing "I Married An Angel"

for Evelyn and Kendell for they first dance.

Evelyn gone put the tissue paper carnations

on the end of each of the pews.

And she gone put white lace all around the paper flowers.

I told Dorothy Jane I was going to

collect them all after the wedding is over.

And use them in a wedding for my dolls.

My favorite is my colored wedding doll.

She look like a chocolate princess who is dressed for a ball.

I wonder if Mama gone let me wear my hair down.

I can see in my mind how pretty I'll be.

I wonder if she gone let me straighten it.

I ain't never had my hair straightened before.

But I think this is the perfect time.

But Mama probably gone put it in a ponytail.

I guess that's still better than me wearing plaits.

Mama treat me like a baby. And I'm seven years old!

I love the socks that Evelyn pick out.

They got a puffy ring of lace that go 'round the ankle.

And she got us all black patent leather shoes

that have a rhinestone buckle on them.

When I get dressed on the day of the wedding,

Mama let my sister do my hair.

Sissy pull my hair from off my face

and clamp the top with a shiny pink barrette.

And she just let it fall down my back.

She use water and grease to make it curly.

I ain't never got to wear my hair down before.

Except that time in the professional picture

that I had took to show off the dress

that Miz Emily got me one year for Easter.

That dress was pink too. Just like my dress for the wedding.

But it have pink flowers on it with green velvet ribbons.

When Evelyn walk in the church that day at the wedding,

she walk down the aisle on Mr. Thompson's arm.

He dressed in a suit and everything.

I ain't never seen him in a suit before.

Because Mr. Thompson don't go to church.

He the only person in Uz who do not go.

Even drunk Miz Rose she go to church.

Mr. Thompson look like he feel uncomfortable.

But he ain't drunk. That's the good thing.

He walk Evelyn down the aisle without falling down.

Evelyn got a big smile on her face.

Just like she got a regular daddy.

Everything go off without a hitch.

Evelyn even change into another dress

when she leave to go on her honeymoon.

I think she say they going to Cancun.

That's a place in Mexico.

I ain't never knowed nobody who went on a honeymoon before.

When my brother Jake got married to Dara,

they just moved in our house into they own bedroom.

I have to leave right after the reception.

Cause Mama and Daddy got to go to church.

So I don't get to collect the tissue paper flowers.

I ask my Mama if she would let me

go in the sanctuary while the reception is going on.

But she just say quit acting so silly.

I try to tell her about my doll wedding and everything.

But she too busy talking to Miz Wendy.

All the people in the wedding party

have to sit at a table in front of everybody else.

So I can't even sneak out or nothing.

And then I see old nasty Dorothy Jane

with all the paper flowers in her hand

when she go and get into they car.

She hold them up so I can see them in the window.

We all pulling out of the parking lot.

Dorothy Jane she stick her tongue out at me.

I shouldn'tna said nothing to her about it.

She mad anyway cause she wudn't in the wedding.

So she just doing this to break my heart.

I slink down in the back seat of the car.

My Mama ask me what is the matter.

I know better than to say anything about the flowers.

So I just grunt and tell her nothing.

"You got the dress. You got to wear your hair down.

And still, you is not satisfied,"

Mama say to me on the way to our church.

I don't say nothing. She don't understand.

Now I can't have my colored wedding doll wedding.

I feel a tear run down my face.

"I know you ain't sitting back there crying."

"Leave her alone," my Daddy say.

My Daddy was the one who married Evelyn.

Cause he a preacher. But not at St. Luke.

He look at me thru the rearview mirror.

"You looked just like a pink angel today,"

my Daddy say. That make me smile.

We get on the highway to go to Little Rock.

My daddy humming "I Married An Angel"
and holding onto my Mama's arm.

Miz Angel Lea

Miz Angel Lea ain't like

no other grandmaw I know.

She wear matching princey slips and girdles

under her usher clothes.

Her underclothes in lots of colors –

yellow, blue, and pink.

My Mama say Miz Angel Lea

just think she slick.

She say the Usher Board colors

suppose to be the purest white.

I hear her and Daddy talking in bed

when we come home last nite.

Daddy say, "Belle, I can't see

anything wrong

with a woman who want to be

a doorkeeper for the Lord."

Mama say, "I 'magine the Lord

don't want no doorkeeper

who spend they time

sleeping with no preacher.

And any other self respecting pastor

would agree with me too."

Mama must not know.

Miz Angel Lea will shoot you.

Everybody know you don't mess with

Miz Angel Lea.

She my friend Sammie's grandmaw.

And Sammie tell me

Miz Angel Lea always

got a gun in her purse.

Sammie say when Miz Angel Lea

stand up and pat her foot,

she getting ready to do something bad.

Right then and there too.

Usually to some crazy woman

who got the nerve to

come in her face, talking 'bout what

Miz Angel Lea is doing with they husband.

She put her gun at they chin

and tell them go talk to they pastor.

Who more likely than not

is one and the same man.

Seem like men of God

is always trying

to sleep with Miz Angel Lea.

Miz Angel Lea say

can't nobody judge her

but the Good Lord His self.

And she His favorite person.

Now run and tell that.

This morning when we get to the door

of New Gospel Temple,

Miz Angel Lea standing there.

She smiling and greeting

every person who enter.

Just like every other Sunday of my life.

You wouldn't even know she got

put out of the church last nite.

Miz Angel Lea tell them Super Saints

she gone go out just like

she did when she come to our church.

"With my head held high,"

Miz Angel Lea say.

"But I will resign,

effective as of this Sunday nite,

as the President of and a Founding Member

of the New Greater Gospel Temple

Missionary Baptist Church Usher Board.

My time is up serving the Lord

in this particular capacity.

And ain't nothing else you can do to me."

But today, she say, she gone come to church.

And she dare anybody to try to stop her.

On this last Sunday she stand regal.

Looking just like a queen.

Her blond hair shining.

Golden just like her skin.

She adjust the white gloves on her hands,

one finger at a time.

She wink at me when I enter.

And she give me a smile.

"How you doing, Little Miss Anderson?"

Miz Angel Lea say.

I say, "I'm doing just fine."

Then Mama snatch me away.

"What she wink at you for?"

my Mama ask me.

"I don't know," I say.

"Just being nice, I think,"

I answer my Mama.

She look at me and she grunt.

Mama know that it's something

going on more than that.

But it's a secret between

Miz Angel Lea and me.

I seen Miz Angel Lea's gun last nite.

And she know that I seen it.

I got tired of sitting on

the hard benches last nite.

Not even the hot chocolate Mama make

or the ice cream pie

was enuf to keep me

sitting still in my seat.

(Mama always make the chi'ren

a real special treat.)

She had made me go to

the Getting Put Out The Church Meeting.

She wouldn't let me go stay

with Sammie and her mama, Miz Aquilla.

Cause Saturday nites the grown folks drink.

And play them evil cards.

(Sammie real name Samonella.

I don't know what her Mama name her that for.

Cause Sissy say Samonella

is some kind of disease.)

Anyway, I was getting real bored

sitting on the church bench.

So Mama tell me to go

and wait for them in the car.

Especially since Miz Angel Lea

hadn't even bothered to show up.

I got up and went outside

while Mama was still on her knees,

talking to her Heavenly Father, Jesus.

I look up and I see

the stars that God had flung

'cross the black velvet sky.

I think God like Arkansas special.

Cause the stars look just like diamonds.

I go get in the back seat

of my Daddy's black Mercury.

It was already nine o'clock,

and I was falling asleep.

I was laying on my back

with my head on the armrest

when I hear a car drive up.

Then I hear a door slam.

I hear high heel shoes clicking

straight across the parking lot.

Then a shadow come by the window,

and I open my eyes up.

I see Miz Angel Lea stop

to make sure her lipstick on right.

She dressed in a two-piece suit

that is a ivory cream white.

She got a hat on the same color

that is cocked to the side.

I see the gun when she

open her purse up wide

to put the lipstick back

into the alligator bag.

I musta moved or something,

cause Miz Angel Lea turn

and she look at me,

smack dab in my face.

The light from the lamppost

reflect off of the grey

metal of the gun. Miz Angel Lea

close up her pocketbook.

Then she wink at me.

The first thing that I thought

as I was drifting off to sleep

was that I don't know nobody

that take a gun to church.

'Cept for my brother Cleophas.

But he crazy so he don't count.

My second thought was that Miz Angel Lea

was gone shoot somebody tonite.

Miz Angel Lea straighten her back.

(I never would have thought

it could have got no straighter.)

Then she walk on up the steps.

I fall asleep and dream of gunslingers

who look like Matt Dillon.

He be on Gunsmoke.

You know, he like Miz Kitty.

But Matt Dillon and Miz Kitty

got angel wings in my dreams.

And they dressed in creamy white

just like Miz Angel Lea.

Miz Angel Lea shake my hand.

She say, "I pray you slept well last nite."

"Yes, M'am," I say.

"I pray you slept well yourself."

"Why, yes I did, Miz Mandy."

She say, "I slept very well indeed.

Thank the Lord," she say.

Mama start down the aisle to her seat.

Then Miz Angel Lea she reach down

and she bend over me

as she give me a big old hug.

"Enjoy the show. I mean

service," Miz Angel Lea laugh.

I hide a giggle with my hands.

Mama come back and snatch me

right there where I'm standing.

"What you and Miz Angel Lea giggling about?"

my Mama ask in her seat.

"Nothing, Mama. We wudn't doing nothing

but exchanging pleasantries

at the door of the Lord's House

like you taught me to do."

"Don't get too full of yo'self.

You a child. So you

need to act like it."

"Yes, Mama," I say.

"And don't get up in grown folks bizness.

You can't always judge folks based

on what you kin see."

Well, if you was to ask me,

that sum the situation up better

than just about anything

that Miz Angel Lea

could ever say in her own defense.

Sometime God have your mouth say

what your heart know is best.

Sammie Lee come to get me.

She hug Mama neck and she say,

"Good Morning, Miz Anderson.

How you doing today?"

Then Sammie go over

and she hug Miz Angel Lea.

Sammie mama, Miz Aquilla,

come over and she speak

to my mama. Mama the First Lady,

so she have to extend her the right hand

of fellowship. Me and Sammie turn

and go up to the choir stand.

Miz Angel Lea start to shouting

when the choir start to sing

Just As I Am.

She fanning her dress tail and screaming.

Everybody looking at her

like she doing it for show.

And don't not one usher come and fan her.

I think that is just wrong.

But Miz Angel Lea don't seem to mind.

She talking in tongues to the Lord.

She running up and down the aisles.

And stamping the floor with her toes.

Her usher uniform heish up.

She got on bright red underneath.

You can tell she in communion

with the Lord by how she look.

The ushers turn they nose up at her.

That don't seem Christian to me.

Let him without sin cast the first stone.

Maybe Jesus was talking 'bout Miz Angel Lea.

Miz Angel Lea stand at the door

of another church now.

She still standing up straight

and being a doorkeeper for the Lord.

And you can still see, I bet,

the color under her uniform.

And I just don't think God mind that.

I don't think He mind that at all.

Freedom Spring

The daffodils dancing

in the front yard like tornadoes.

Red roses climb, wild,

to the roof of our house.

This Mother's Day is alive

with hope and with morning.

'Cept for the slash that is running

'cross my Mama mouth.

She kneading the dough

for the biscuits for breakfast.

She got the radio on.

Tune to WOKJ.

That's the radio station

where my brother, Quint, is a DJ.

They talking 'bout the Freedom Riders.

Colored folks and whites

riding buses down South

from Washington D.C. to New Orleans.

All of them is students.

My Mama say,

"This how these chir'en choose to spend

they spring vacation?

They ought to be home with they mamas."

Then she whip the dough

like it's the thing made her mad.

The sun is shining

like a bag full of diamonds.

Coming thru our dining room window

in long, shiny strands.

What Mama really mad about

is that Quinton is with them.

He working on the radio.

Reporting everything

that go on. We ain't heard nothing

from him yet so far this morning.

Mama keep sucking her teeth.

And saying, "Hmmpfh, hmmpfh. Hmmpfh, hmmpfh."

Ain't nothing we done

to try to make her happy

on her special day

done worked out at all.

Not the talcum powder I buy her

with my babysitting money.

Not the earrings from Sissy.

Not the perfume from Jake.

Not one thing that we planned

has made her one bit of difference.

Sissy say, "Let me cook the biscuits, Mama.

You're supposed to take

it easy today." Mama say,

"Sissy, you know I don't let nobody cook my biscuits.

Wash that pan out there for me.

Mandy, you gone out and play."

See now I know something up.

Cause this is a Sunday morning.

I don't play outside on a Sunday.

Never did. Never have.

We don't do nothing but get ready

for church on Sunday morning.

It must be something she want to say to Sissy.

And she don't want me to hear.

So I go out the front door

and run around to the back.

I sit outside the kitchen window.

The only thing about that

is that Cud'n Stell can see me

if she laying in her bed.

And that's the only place

she be at.

So she gone tell Mama

where I am.

But, 'til then, I'ma sit here

and be quiet as a mouse.

Sissy see me thru the screen,

but she don't open up her mouth.

"What Quinton say when he call

on the telephone this morning?"

"He didn't talk to me long.

He said things have started going bad."

"What kind of bad?

He say anythang else?"

"No, he just said to listen to the radio."

I feel a spider on my leg.

I reach down and brush it off.

It run thru the grass like a monster.

Legs spreading all over,

every which away all at once.

The grass so green and sparkling,

seem like it's been sprinkle with sunshine.

Strange how things can be so beautiful

and so scary all at once.

Mama voice been heavy

with sanctified songs this Sunday morning.

Her voice carry out the window.

> *Hear my humble cry*
>
> *Whilst on others thou art calling*
>
> *Do not pass me by*

The Freedom Riders riding

on the Greyhound and the Trailways.

Eleven days they been together.

Even sitting on the same seat.

Today they is suppose to

finally get to Alabama.

When they get to where they going,

they always go in to eat

at the white lunch counter.
So far, it ain't been no trouble.
White folks done closed the counter
in some places.
But they ain't done nothing
more than that.
We done watched it
on the television.
They on the 6:00 news
every evening.
Plus Quinton been doing
his coverage.
He call it a
eye witness report.

Mama say he a fool.
"Don't he know
white folks is crazy?
They care less
about a colored
than 'bout the dirt
on they feet."
But Quinton live
in Birmingham,
so it ain't nothing
Mama can do about it.
Just keep the radio tuned
to his station.

Mama yell, "Mandy!
Come and eat!"

I go round the front
like I ain't been listening to nothing.
I walk thru the front door.
Just as cool as you please.
Mama say, "Mandy when I tell you
to do something, I mean it.
And don't start lying and make it worse.
You got grass on your knees
where you been sitting by the window.
Wash yo' hands. Quit being hardheaded.
I got enough to think about
without worrying about you today."
I start walking down the hall
on the way to the bathroom.
Then we hear Quinton's voice.
And we all freeze where we at.

"The Greyhound bus just pulled
into the Anniston station.
It's the stop before Birmingham.
And there is a mob of white men outside.
They are screaming profanities
and breaking out the back window of the bus."
Then we hear a big explosion.
Then, "Let's burn them niggers alive."

Quinton start to sound

like his voice full of panic.

He say, "The bus is on fire!

The bus is on fire!

The gas tank just exploded.

The mob has started to flee.

The Freedom Riders and other passengers

are all trapped inside.

And I can hear breaking glass.

Wait! I see

the door is open.

The riders are pouring outside.

They are gasping for air.

Some of them are falling to the ground.

I can hear moans for water.

And there is no one to help.

Wait. I see a little white girl

coming through the crowd

with some water.

She just walked over

to a Negro woman

and put a towel on her face.

Now she's giving her a glass.

This is a child of 12 or 13.

She is the only one who is helping.

She is moving from place to place.

She is giving every Negro

she encounters a glass of water.

When she is sure they're all right,

she then moves on to the next."

Mama say, "Amazing Grace!"

Quinton say, "This is amazing.

This little child has surely saved a life today.

The mob is starting to come back

in the direction of the bus.

Someone just hit a Negro man

on the ground with a club.

The Negro is using the towel

that the little girl gave him

to wipe his face.

His face is covered with blood."

Then the radio go silent.

We all look at one another.

Then Mama she start to singing.

Her voice sound like a sigh.

> *I'm calling you, Saviour*
>
> *Blessed saviour*
>
> *Hear my humble cry*
>
> *Whilst on others thou are calling*
>
> *Do not pass my chile by*

Her voice break at the end.

She just stand there looking at the radio.

Like it is color TV.

Don't none of us know what to say.

We just look at one another.

We don't know what happen to Quinton.

Don't know if he got hit.

Don't know if he safe.

Mama say, "Let's sit down to eat."

So we all take our places.

Uncle Jesse come out his bedroom

and go fix him a plate.

Ain't none of the rest of us hungry.

Uncle Jesse take his plate back to the bedroom.

He don't never eat at the table.

Uncle Jesse is real strange.

Lucky suck his two fingers.

He always do that when he nervous.

Or whenever he scared.

That's bout the only way that you know.

I start to crying.

"Mama, what happen to Quinton?"

Mama say, "Ain't nothing happen to Quinton.

He fine. I just know it.

Eat yo' breakfast

so you can start getting ready."

"I don't want to go to church.

Not 'til I'm sho' my brother safe."

Sissy say, "Don't you worry."

But she ain't looking at me.

Her eyes is all watery.

And she looking down at her plate.

And I can see the tear drop

into her tomato preserves.

I touch it with my finger.

And Sissy smile a sad smile.

Then she reach over and kiss me

on the tippy top of my forehead.

"Pray, Mandy," she say.

"You just pray real hard."

The radio done fill

the whole room with its silence.

Not even the sun shining like diamonds

can lift the despair in the room.

Everything in me is screaming

that the white mob done got Quinton.

I can see it in my mind.

He all bloody and wounded.

The radio start to crackle.

Now we can hear static.

Like something under water

trying to make its presence known.

We all hold our breaths.

Waiting to hear from my brother.

"Our sound engineer

has been wounded," Quinton say.

You can hear all our breath

explode like a bomb.

"As if on cue," Quinton say,

"the white mob all dispersed.

Rev. Shuttlesworth has shown up

with some members of his church.

There are about 5 cars.

Each one of them are filled

with the dozen or so Freedom Riders.

Tho some are wounded, they are all well

enough to walk on their own.

We are moving away.

We will bring you more

breaking news later on today.

Right now, we are all going

to Rev. Shuttlesworth's church.

Looks like the Freedom Rides are over.

These students are hurt.

And have all decided

they cannot continue this trip.

There has been talk from some corners

that there are replacements here.

But I cannot confirm that.

Stay tuned for more breaking news.

We will be reporting next from Birmingham,

the next stop on the tour.

What a day this has been!

These young students have stood strong!

I wish to all of you out there

a pleasant Mother's Day morning.

This is Quinton Delacortes Anderson

for WOKJ.

Your Civil Rights news station."

"God sho' is good," my Mama say.

Fat Plaits And Ashy Knees

My Mama say when she a girl

and she go to school,

way back when,

sometime back in a whole 'nother century,

that only the white chi'ren get to ride on the bus.

Colored chi'ren have to walk.

And the white kids pass by

and chunk mud rocks at them.

She say the school that she go to

is 'bout 10 miles each way.

But every time she tell the story,

the school get further and further.

I done heard this story

for so much of my life,

I can tell it by heart.

I am dusting the floorboards

in the living room.

And oiling our beautiful

old wooden upright piano.

These the two things

I have to do every Saturday.

Along with wringing the clothes

from out our new wringer washer

and hanging them out

on the clothesline in the backyard.

Mama sitting on the couch

sewing my new dress for school.

The television is on.

Filled with black and white images

of little colored chi'ren

trying to desegregate schools.

Mama say, "We traipsed down long roads

where dust rose up when we walked.

Or they was muddy in the springtime

because of the rain.

In the winter, them roads

would be hard as a rock.

And we walked 'em barefoot

for most of the year.

In the wintertime we would cut us out

some cardboard foot shapes,

and put them down in the bottom

of our shoes to make soles.

 It didn't do much for warmth.

But I woulda did anything.

Walked that much and further.

Just to go to school.

Chi'ren today is ungrateful.

That's just what y'all is."

Seem like every story she tell

seem to come back to this.
"You got buses that will take you
to yo' very own schools.
But you rather go to school with chi'ren
who don't even want you near them."
We watching pictures on the television
of colored chi'ren on a bus.
And these white women trying to turn it over.
And they screaming and they fussing.
I ain't never seen white women
who look so mad and so mean.
These is white mamas.
With chi'ren I coulda played with
when my mama took me with her
to they house to clean.

All them chi'ren want to do
is go to school. Like my Mama.
Why white people hate us so much?
That's what I want to know.
My mama say this gone happen.
But I didn't believe it.
So I filled out the form
and decided to go
to the white school in Jacksonville.
But my Mama don't know it.
She think I'm going to the colored school
where I done always went.

But after seeing all these chi'ren on TV

getting turned over in buses,

I'm starting to have second thoughts.

I don't know what to think.

All summer long

my head done been hurting.

Cause when Mama find out

she gone give me a whipping.

Cause when they give us

the Freedom of Choice cards to sign,

I write her name where it say parents.

If my Daddy was alive,

I know he woulda gave me

permission to go.

Cause my daddy for integration.

But my mama say no.

But President Johnson done got

the Civil Rights bill sign.

That mean now I can go to school

wherever I decide.

So me and Jewel decide

we gone do something new.

So when them cards come in the mail,

me and Jewel decide to

sign our mamas names on them

Freedom of Choice cards.

That say now we going to school

in Jacksonville, Arkansas.

That's the nearest white school

to where I live out in the County.

And all a Negro child need now

is permission from they parents.

Mama say she ain't never heard

of nothing so stupid.

And what I'm seeing on television

now is making me wonder.

Seeing this happen, it change me.

Now I know just like Mama always say

that I'm somebody who can be kill.

A little colored girl. Me.

With my fat plaits

and my ashy knees.

I'm gone have to tell my Mama

soon what I did.

Mama call my name

and I come back with a jerk.

She tell me to come over where she at

so I can try on the skirt

that she sewing for me.

I walk slow cross the floor

with tears shining in my eyes.

"What is you crying for?"

my Mama ask me.

But I can't say a word.

She say, "You see now what I tell you?"
I see little kids in the dirt
with they new school clothes all messed up
from the mud on the ground.
So I know I got to tell her.
But I can't tell her now.
I'm gone have to wait
'til all them images is gone.
When she ain't looking so sad.
I feel a headache coming on.

"You like your new dress, Mandy?"
Mama look at me and say.
"Yes, Mama," I say,
to the throb of my headache.
Mama take the pins out the dress.
One of them stick my skin.
And I burst into tears.
But I still can't tell my Mama
about the trouble I'm in.
Mama hold me in her arms
and she just let me cry.
And that make me know
everything gone be all right.

My Daddy Dead

Driving to church
that Sunday morning,
all of us was in
Quinton's new pink Pontiac.
The one with the
backlight fins.
The radio is full of static.
All the windows
rolled up and closed.
I feel like I got on
some kind of armour
instead of my
new Easter clothes.

I'm sitting between
Quint and Mama
in the middle of
the front seat.
And Twinkie and Lulu
sitting in the back.
Directly in back of me.
On each side of them
sit Lucky and Sissy.
So we can't let

the windows down.
Cause Sissy say the wind
gone blow her hair.
And she ain't walking in church
looking like no clown.
She say with this
new hairstyle
she need every strand
 to stay in place.
Her hair is comb like
one of them Beatles.
Comb to the front.
Down in her face.
The air in the car
is hot and clammy
from everybody taking up
air to breathe.
Ever so often
my niece Twinkie cough.
And her sister LuLu
start to sneeze.

"Mama," I say,
"Can't we open the window?"
I like Sissy and all.
But my head 'bout to blow.
Mama say, "Mandy, don't start worrying me

'bout them windows.

And don't let me have to tell you

that no mo'."

I don't know why Sissy hair

mean more to Mama than my breath.

I got myself a sick headache.

And I hurt down in my neck.

My eyes is watering

like I'm seeing things.

And my stomach

it is churning.

And I got a smell

in the back of my nose

that smell just like

a house is burning.

All of us

got on two-piece suits.

Mama's is the color

of a deep dark rose.

And she got on a hat

that's the exact same color.

With a veil that reach

down to her nose.

Aunt Ree make the hat

that Mama is wearing.

Mama she make the suit.

Her hat cocked so her

silver widow peak show

where it's done greyed

down to the roots.

All the hats

that Mama wear lately

done had some kind of

veil on them.

Until today,

she been dressing in black.

But, today, she say

we gone all start to live.

I thought living was what

we had been doing.

Every day

and all the while.

But today, somehow,

is suppose to be different.

I can see it in the way

my Mama smile.

The radio is blaring

to be heard over the static.

In between the

church songs they been

talking about some

colored marchers

crossing over the

Edmund Pettus Bridge.

It's some Negroes down to
Selma, Alabama.
Mama reach over me
to turn the knob and say,
"I can tell by the noise
that's in this static
that this gone be a
real bad day."

Ever so often,
I look over at Quinton.
His face wear something
look like a smile.
I'm trying to look anywhere
but the highway.
I'm getting sicker
with every mile.
 "Can't we at least
crack a window, Mama?"
I'm gone die anyway
so I ask her again.
"Mandy, hush up,"
Mama say.
Then she lean across me
as she bend
over even more closer
to hear the radio better.
I want to tell her to get up.

But what can I do?

So I just sit there

like a dummy.

Feel like her elbow

gone go straight thru

the big bone in my leg.

But do Mama care?

She just continue

to use my thigh

like, to her, it ain't nothing

no more than a armrest.

I feel like I'm about to cry.

Mama say, "God gone make things

better for coloreds

bye and bye.

Up in the sky."

Quint say, "But colored folks

is tired of waiting."

Mama say, "Tired ain't no reason

for folks to die."

Quint say, "It's time for Negroes

to stand up for themselves

and help God on

this path to freedom."

Mama say, "And them white folks

on that bridge is saying

if you can't join 'em,

then you might as well beat 'em.

And don't go blaspheming,

Quinton Delacortes,

the Holy Name

Of The Lord."

"I ain't blaspheming

nothing, Mama.

I'm just repeating what

God say in His word."

I think when they get

to the other side of the bridge,

they gone kneel down

and pray to God above.

And sing the Civil Rights

National Anthem.

It's a song that's call

"We Shall Overcome."

Everywhere you go

and all on the radio,

seem like coloreds

is singing the song's refrain.

Rev. Jasmine is playing it

on the radio.

I feel a storm

inside my brain.

Quint say, "Colored people trying

to change the world.

And all the bad things

going on in it."

Maybe things is changing

somewhere up North.

But far in the world

as I can see in it,

everything going on

the same way it was.

And folks in Uz

don't see nothing wrong with it.

Colored folks in Uz

still get up off they seats

and let the white folks

sit down in them.

I done been raise that way

all of my life.

It ain't even been nothing

I done never found

time to think or worry about.

In Uz, chi'ren get up

to let *everybody* sit down.

Daddy tell me, "Mandy,

now you look close.

Cause you watching history

fixing to be made."

Mama say, "Hush talking to that chile

'bout that foolishness.
Long as I live
on this side of the grave
ain't no chile of mine
gone be caught up in this mess.
Grown folk ought to know better.
But the chir'en they don't.
And long as God
leave breath in me
you can be show n'an one
of my chil'ren won't
never be mix up
in this Civvie Rights mess."
She hold my head
close to her breast.
"The chi'ren marching
cause they tired," Daddy say,
"of being treated like
they something less.
Ain't your chi'ren
suppose to have
the same things that God
bless the white chi'ren with?"
Mama say, "A.D.
that's what y'all don't see.
God done bless me
with His breath.
He bless me when He

woke me up this morning.

Dress and clothe

in my right mind.

God blessing me

in spite of white folks.

Been blessing me.

All the time.

And you couldn't pay me

to sit behind that counter

up to Franklin Department Store.

I done see'd that man

stand behind that counter

pick up food from off the floor

and put it on them

white folks plate.

Just as nasty as he can be.

So why I want to eat

behind white folks?

You tell me what

that's gone gain me."

Daddy say, "Belle,

that ain't the point…"

"That's the point exactly

far as I can see.

The Bible say wherever you is,

content is what you s'pose to be."

Daddy say, "Belle, you know

being second class citizens

ain't what the apostle meant.

You can look all thru the Bible.

Moses came cause

the people wudn't content.

Didn't in the Bible, God return

His chosen people's captivity?

God mean His people to be whole.

God mean His people to be free."

"Shush! Shush!" Mama say.

Rev. Jasmine, the DJ,

he done start to talk again

about them Negroes

down to Selma

and they walk

across that bridge.

It seem like we ain't gone

never get to church.

Never get out this car

and this long, stuffy ride.

Quinton exit on Ninth Street

off the freeway.

My eyes watering with tears.

And I feel like crying.

Ninth Street in Little Rock

is a whole different world.

Colored women dress up

and go to smoky clubs

and dance with some other

woman's husband.

At the Lucky Lady,

you can play the numbers.

And bet on the dogs.

Most people live in apartments

on this part of Ninth Street.

And they don't wake up in time

to send they chi'ren to church.

Even thru the closed windows,

I can hear the games they playing.

One group of heathen chi'ren

standing out on they stoop

in front of one of they

apartment buildings.

They playing a game I play

sometime with Jewel or Brenda Nell.

Sometime we play it

after school in the yard.

It's a game that's call

Aint Dinah Dead.

>Aint Dinah dead, the leader call.

>How she die? the others say.

>O she died like this, the leader answer.

Then she twist her body all kinds of ways

to show what Dinah looked like when she died.

>O she died like this, the other chi'ren say.

And the one who can't do like
the leader the worse
got to be "It"
the next time we play.

I can hear the game
the heathen chi'ren playing
ringing over and over
in my head.
We finally get to the church
and I jump out the car.
I bend over and breathe in
great big gulps of air.
Sissy say, "Mandy,
are you all right?"
"No, Sissy. I been sick
this whole long ride."
Then Mama walk up.
She grab my arm
and pull me over
to the side.

She say, "Mandy, I ain't fuh
none of yo' foolishness.
I particular ain't fuh
n'an one of yo' fits."
"I can't help it,"
I tell Mama.

"My head is hurting

and I'm feeling sick."

Just then Sammie

Rain walk up.

"Y'all better

hurry up," she say.

I look at Mama

thru the fog in my head.

Curtis done already

start to play

the processional music.

Since today is Easter,

ain't none of us

gone wear our robes.

That way all of us

that's in the choir

can show off our

new Easter clothes.

My head is pounding.

I can't hardly walk.

Sammie reach and pull me

by the arm.

We rush into the choir room

and take our places

just as Curtis play

the last opening chords.

The song of the heathen chi'ren

still ringing in my head.
So I keep messing
up the beat.
I'm dipping and stepping
when I ought to be swaying.
I feel real shaky
on my feet.

When I finally walk thru
the door into the sanctuary,
the very first thing
that catch my eye
is the Pastor's chair
that belong to my Daddy.
I catch my breath.
And I start to cry.

They done took the black mourning cloth
from off my Daddy chair!
This is just not
suppose to be.
And if it *was*
suppose to happen,
seem like somebody
coulda at least told me!
I still cannot
believe my eyes.
When a Pastor die,

they drape his chair in black
for a mourning period
of at least six months.
My Daddy ain't been dead
for three months yet.

The whole church
stand up with the choir.
Over the organ, you can hear
the sound of shuffling feet.
I look over at the pew
where sit my Mama.
She will not even so much
as look at me.
Cause she know she wrong
for how this happen.
She coulda at least gave me
some kind of warning.
Now I know why
she sit in Daddy chair
when she say the blessing
at breakfast this morning.
Ain't nobody never sit
in my Daddy chair.
His place done always been
at the head of the table.
He wudn't the kind of man
who was gone miss a meal.

I thought Mama cried cause

she finally missed him this morning.

But what she really was saying,

I see now,

is that this the day when

Daddy no longer have a place.

Not at our table.

And not at our church.

The only place my Daddy

got now is a grave.

Down in the ground.

Up under the earth.

Ain't nothing left of him now

but his rotting body.

When I close my eyes,

I can see, like yesterday,

the pallbearers as they

tenderly carry his body

out of the church

after the second funeral Down Home.

I can hear the gravediggers

scooping dirt from out the ground.

Tears is running

down my face.

I look at Mama.

And she frown.

All I can hear in my head

is the heathen chi'ren's song.

And the game they was playing

'bout Aint Dinah dead.

You know how sometime

you hear a song

and can't seem to get it

from out your head?

That's what it's like

for me this morning.

Rev. Long say,

"Today we celebrating Jesus

being raised from the dead.

And now it's time for us

to pause in the program

so the chi'ren can get

they speeches said."

Miz Angel Lea get up

from off the front pew.

She the Mistress of Ceremony

for the Easter program.

"Er-rer," Miz Angel Lea

clear her throat.

"Can the church give us

another A-man?"

"A-man,"

the congregation say.

"Speak thru her, Lord,"

Miz Caroline groan.

Miz Angel Lea ask the choir

for a "A" and "B" selection.

The music from the organ

sound like a moan.

Curtis start to play

"Just As I Am."

He raise his hands

and the choir stand up.

Everybody, that is,

except for me.

I can't seem to move.

Feel like I'm stuck.

I can hear the kids in the

audience out there laughing.

I look at Mama.

I can tell she mad.

Cause I'm embarrassing

her in the public.

Mama look like she want to

go up side my head.

"Sang, Bessie,"

Miz Caroline say.

"Sang the song."

The church all on they feet.

When the choir finish singing

and everybody sit down,

Sammie Lee have to

pull me to my seat.

"The first selection is by

little Miss Cora Lee Sanders,"

Miz Angel Lea say.

"Come on, baby, and say your speech."

Cora Lee mama push

her to the front.

Cora Lee can't be

no more than three.

And she shame-face

in front of the congregation.

"Say your speech, baby,"

Miz Sanders say.

Cora Lee mutter something

and run back to her seat.

"A-man! A-man!"

the church all say.

"And the next selection

is a special treat.

Miss Amanda Denise Anderson will bring us her own unique rendition

of that great Negro sermon

by James Weldon Johnson.

That timeless standard

called, "The Creation."

The whole church applaud.

They been waiting for this.

I done done

The Creation before.

But when I stand up

in the choir stand,

my feet feel like

they ain't quite touching the floor.

Last year for the Christmas program,

I did this speech.

Everybody say it was the best thing

they done ever seen.

I walk slow to take my place

in front of the pulpit.

My head is bowed.

And I'm feeling mean.

The first line go,

'And God stepped out...'

So I turn away from the audience

so when I turn back around

I can step out like

I'm as mysterious as God.

I ball my hands into a fist.

And I open my mouth.

But what come out is,

> "My Daddy dead
>
> How he die?
>
> O, he died like this..."

123

I hadn't intended
to say them words.
Seem like something just
come over me.
And if that
wudn't bad enuf,
I acted it out
for the whole church to see.
I clutched my chest
just like my Daddy did
on that Sunday when
he had his heart attack.
He had just
finished up his sermon.
He was doing the
benediction, in fact.
I flailed my arms
out to the sides.
Stepped back two steps
like I was about to fall.
That Sunday when Daddy
had his attack in the pulpit,
the church rose as one
and, as one, they called
out, "Catch him! Catch him!
Somebody catch him!
Don't let him fall

and hit his head!"
Deacon Morgan was
the first to reach him.
But by the time he got there,
my Daddy was dead.

The whole church
was in confusion.
"Hush! Hush!"
Miz Caroline cry out.
I slowly come
from out the fog
and realize it's now
that I'm hearing her shout.
My ears is ringing
in my head.
Miz Sella Mae running
up and down the aisles.
Everybody else looking over
at my Mama
to see what she gone do
'bout her youngest child.
Seem like I can see
everybody's reaction.
All of a sudden,
and all at once.
I feel like, for the first time,
I can really see.

Not just what's on people's face.

But what's in they hearts.

Mama's gray streak shining

in the sunlight.

The rays is bouncing

from off her hair.

The sunbeams shining

thru the stained glass window

bounce off her head

and into the air.

Her face is twist

in perfect agony.

The tears she cried this morning

done start to flow again.

She allow them to run

free down her face.

Then she fix her mouth

in a bitter grin.

Then Mama open her mouth wide

and she holler.

It's a high-pitch mewling,

put you in mind of a cat.

The birds outside

fly into the windows.

The ushers run to where

my Mama is at.

They fan her with some fans

that we got from the funeral home;

I think they come

from Ruffin and Jarrett.

The sound Mama make

come from high in her throat.

The birds outside

can't seem to bear it.

Everybody looking at her

like she uncovering they shame.

The whole congregation

is crying in they seats.

One thing I can say about

what's happening with Mama

is that it's done took

all the attention from off of me.

So I run down the aisle

and out the front door.

I'm too sick to cry.

And I'm too tired to sing.

Besides that, I'm just about

sick and tired of crying.

Seem like crying

is all I done been

doing since my Daddy died.

My heart is tired

from missing my Daddy.

And I'm tired of people treating him

like he ain't never lived.

Inside the church,

I can hear Sister Sadie

starting up a old

Dr. Watts hymn.

I can still hear Mama

in betwixt the singing.

Her voice sound like something

I ain't never heard.

Sound like a animal

that's been wounded.

Or like a little baby bird

that's done fell from out the nest

and been stepped on.

But not crushed hard enuf

for it to die.

(That whole long week –

even with Daddy's two funerals –

I didn't never once

see my Mama cry.)

I run out the church

into the parking lot.

I lift my hair

to get some air on my neck.

I go round the back

to the back of the church

and lean my head

up against the brick.

My stomach rumble

from deep in my gut.

My mouth it start

to fill up with spit.

"Help me, Jesus.

Help me, God."

The prayer bubble up

from off my lips.

Seem like the whole

wide world is spinning.

I feel myself

falling to the ground.

And then, just like that!

in the blink of a eye,

I feel myself being lifted

by the neck and turned around.

I see a woman

bright as the sunlight.

I turn to the presence

at my side.

Her garment is of

a bright, shiny material

that put you in mind

of a beautiful bride.

She dressed in a flowing,

clingy gauze-like fabric.

And on her head,

she wear a crown

that's sprinkled with

the moon and stars.

The angel look me

up and down.

She say, "His ways

ain't our ways.

Nor is His thoughts

our thoughts."

"What do that mean?"

I ask.

But the angel

do not say.

She already disappearing

in front of my eyes.

Her last words is,

"Don't forget to pray."

I'm so scared,

I'm seeing double.

All I can do is

stand and stare

off into space

with my mouth open.

When Sammie come out,

I'm still standing there.

I walk to the car

with Sammie holding me up.
The wind feel like fingers
playing in my hair.
I keep reaching up
and touching the back of my neck.
Like I think I'm gone find
a hand back there.
Mama standing by the car
talking to Brother Green.
She look at me
with what feel like shame.
Her hat done come off
and her hair hanging loose.
And I decide right then
that she the one to blame
for all the pain
that I been feeling.
Cause she won't sit down
and talk to me.
If I ain't the baby girl
of the Pastor,
then who is I'm
suppose to be?

Mama look at me
and her eyes say it all.
I'm gone have to pay
for what I did in church.

She look totally
disgusted with me.
Like she sorry she ever took
the time out to birth
a daughter that treat her
bad as me.
She motion for me
to get in the car.
I get in the back seat
by the door this time.
I grab the handle and roll
the window down as far
as it will go.
The air cool on my face.
At least for the ride home,
I'm gone get to breathe.
Breathing ain't something
I'm gone be doing long, I bet.
Cause when I get home,
Mama gone kill me dead.

I keep hearing the words
and the voice of the angel
ringing over and over,
all thru my head.
"His ways is not our ways.
Nor is His thoughts our thoughts."
Then I remember the other words

that the angel said.

On the radio they say

it was bad for the marchers.

Bloody Sunday they calling

this Easter day.

Many Negroes was injured.

Maybe some even dead.

So I bow my head.

And I begin to pray.

Made in the USA
Coppell, TX
23 January 2021